Karl Jenkins

A Parliament of Owls
A celebration of collective nouns

for mixed chorus, saxophone,
percussion & piano duet

Words by Carol Barratt

Vocal score

BOOSEY & HAWKES

Boosey & Hawkes Music Publishers Ltd
www.boosey.com

Published by Boosey & Hawkes Music Publishers Ltd
Aldwych House
71–91 Aldwych
London
WC2B 4HN

www.boosey.com

an  company

© Copyright 2005 by Boosey & Hawkes Music Publishers Ltd

ISMN 979-0-060-12073-2
ISBN 978-0-85162-608-6

First published for sale 2010

Printed in England by The Halstan Printing Group, Amersham, Bucks

Cover design by RF Design UK Limited
Owl illustration: Micha Archer/istockphoto.com
Music origination by Jon Bunker

Commissioned by the 3rd Yoxford Arts Festival

First performed on 20 August 2005 at Yoxford Church, Suffolk, UK,
by the Choir of New College, Oxford, with Karl Jenkins and Carol Barratt (piano duet),
Nigel Hitchcock (saxophone), Paul Clarvis and Dave Hassell (percussion),
conducted by Edward Higginbottom

CONTENTS

I Irresistible and noisy 1

II Quietly sitting still 18

III Monstrous mayhem.. 28

A Parliament of Owls

A celebration of collective nouns

I – Irresistible and noisy

A Company of Parrots
Irresistible and noisy
As *A Party of Jays*
In the morning haze.
As the parrots start to party
In the company of jays,
You can hear *A Peep of Chickens*
Irresistible and noisy
As *A Gaggle of Geese*
Does its party-piece.
hiss hiss hiss hissssssssssss
A Company of Parrots
Irresistible and noisy
As *A Mustering of Storks*
Taking lunchtime walks.
Irresistible and noisy
As *A Party of Jays*
Chatters as it plays.

II – Quietly sitting still

A Parliament of Owls
Meets from time to time
With *A Bouquet of Pheasants*
Standing in a line.
Close by, *A Charm of Finches*
Quietly sitting still
As *A Piteousness of Doves*
Discusses how to trill.

A Kindle of Kittens
Hurries out of sight
As *A Convocation of Eagles*
Hovers like a kite.
And quietly sitting still
Like *A Sloth of Bears*
You can spot *A Knot of Toads*
But no-one really cares!

And *An Ostentation of Peacocks*
Gives a bird's eye point of view
As *A Parliament of Owls*
Wisely calls, tu-whit, tu-whoo.
And quietly sitting still
As parliament adjourns
A Knot of Toads starts croaking
And voices its concerns.

Ein Eulenparlament

Ein Lob der Kollektiva★

I – Unwiderstehlich und lärmend

Eine Papageiengesellschaft,
Unwiderstehlich und lärmend
Wie *Eine Häherparty*
Im Morgendunst.
Wenn die Papageien ihre Party
In der Gesellschft der Häher beginnen,
Hört man *Ein Hühnerpiepen,*
Unwiderstehlich und lärmend,
Während *Ein Gänsegeschnatter*
Sein Partylied singt.
Zisch zisch zisch zischschschsch
Eine Papageiengesellschaft,
Unwiderstehlich und lärmend
Wie *Eine Storchenversammlung*
Auf ihrem Mittagsspaziergang.
Unwiderstehlich und lärmend
Wie *Eine Häherparty*
Beim Spielen schnattert.

II – Still dasitzend

Ein Eulenparlament
Trifft sich von Zeit zu Zeit
Mit *Einem Fasanenbukett,*
Das in einer Reihe steht.
Nahebei *Ein Finkenzauber,*
Der still dasitzt,
Während *Ein Taubenelend*
Bespricht, wie man zu trillern hat.

Ein Kätzchenwurf
Huscht eilig ins Versteck,
Während *Eine Adlerzusammenkunft*
Hoch wie ein Drachen schwebt.
Und still dasitzend
Wie *Eine Bärenträgheit*
Sieht man *Einen Krötenknoten,*
Aber niemanden kümmert es!

Und *Ein Pfauenprunk*
Trägt bei zur Vogelperspektive,
Während *Ein Eulenparlament*
Weise ruft, huhu, huhu.
Und still dasitzend,
Während sich das Parlament vertagt,
Beginnt *Ein Krötenknoten* zu quaken
Und äußert seinen Vorbehalt.

Un parlement de chouettes

Hommage aux noms collectifs[†]

I – Irrésistible et tapageuse

Une compagnie de perroquets
Irrésistible et tapageuse
Comme *une fête de geais*
Dans la brume du matin.
Alors que les perroquets commencent la fête
En compagnie des geais,
On entend *un pépiement de poussins*
Irrésistible et tapageur
Tandis qu'*un cacardement d'oies*
Donne son récital.
Hiss hiss hiss hissssssssssss
Une compagnie de perroquets
Irrésistible et tapageuse
Comme *un défilé de cigognes*
Marchant pendant son déjeuner ;
Irrésistible et tapageuse
Comme *une fête de geais*
Bavarde tout en jouant.

II – Calmement assis en silence

Un parlement de chouettes
Se réunit de temps à autre
Avec *une floraison de faisans*
Debout en ligne.
Non loin, *une chaînette de pinsons*
Calmement assise en silence
Comme *un réconfort de tourterelles*
Débat de la manière de triller.

Un éclat de chatons
File hors de vue
Tandis qu'*une formation d'aigles*
Plane comme un cerf-volant.
Et calmement assis en silence
Comme *un amassement d'ours*
On repère *un nœud de crapauds*
Mais personne ne s'y intéresse !

Et *une parade de paons*
Donne le point de vue des oiseaux
Alors qu'*un parlement de chouettes*
Appelle avec sagesse, hou-hou, hou-hou.
Et calmement assis en silence
Alors que le parlement lève la séance
Un nœud de crapauds commence à croasser
Et exprime ses inquiétudes.

[*]Anmerkung des Übersetzers: Anschauliche Kollektiva, dh Sammelnamen für Gruppen von Tieren der gleichen Art, sind eine englische Spezialität. Während das Deutsche vorwiegend allgemein verständliche Sammelbegriffe kennt [eine Gruppe von Gänsen, im Deutschen eine Gänseschar, heißt im Englischen zB *a gaggle of geese*, wörtlich: ein Gänsegeschnatter], haben sich im Englischen bildhafte Bezeichnungen eingebürgert, die im Folgenden wörtlich übertragen wurden.

[†]Note de la traduceuse : Jeux de mots sur les expressions anglaises désignant les animaux en groupe prises dans leur sens littéral.

III – Monstrous mayhem

Monstrous mayhem, monstrous mayhem.

A *Murder of Crows* and nobody knows
What to do or when it flew.

A *Bus'ness of Ferrets* can anyone tell it
When to race or what to chase.

Monstrous mayhem, evil and black,
A *Skulk of Foxes* on the attack.

Monstrous mayhem, monstrous mayhem.

A *Descent of Woodpeckers* joins the fray,
Monstrous mayhem, all in a day.

An *Unkindness of Ravens, A Murder of Crows*.
When did it start? Nobody knows,

Except

A *Pod of Whales*
A *Crash of Rhinos*
A *Pride of Lions*
A *Trip of Goats*
A *Shrewdness of Apes*
A *Leap of Leopards*
A *Sloth of Bears*
A *Bouquet of Pheasants*
A *Knot of Toads*
A *Party of Jays*
A *Kindle of Kittens*
A *Gaggle of Geese*

And of course,

A *Parliament of Owls*.

Tu-whit, tu-whoo.

Carol Barratt

III – Wahnwitziger Wirrwarr

Wahnwitziger Wirrwarr, wahnwitziger Wirrwarr.

Ein Krähenmord und niemand weiß,
Was tun oder wohin er flog.

Ein Frettchenumtrieb: Kann ihm jemand sagen,
Wann man rennt oder wen man jagt.

Wahnwitziger Wirrwarr, böse und schwarz,
Ein Fuchshinterhalt greift an.

Wahnwitziger Wirrwarr, wahnwitziger Wirrwarr.

Ein Spechteabstieg mischt sich ein,
Wahnwitziger Wirrwarr, den ganzen Tag.

Eine Rabenbosheit, Ein Krähenmord.
Wann fing das an? Keiner weiß es,

Außer

Einer Walschote,
Einem Nashornzusammenstoß,
Einem Löwenstolz,
Einem Ziegengang,
Einem Affenscharfsinn,
Einem Leopardensprung,
Einer Bärenträgheit,
Einem Fasanenbukett,
Einem Krötenknoten,
Einer Häherparty,
Einem Kätzchenwurf,
Einem Gänsegeschnatter

Und natürlich

Einem Eulenparlament.

Huhu, huhu.

Carol Barratt
Übersetzung: Bernd Müller

III – Pagaille monstrueuse

Pagaille monstrueuse, pagaille monstrueuse.

Un complot de corneilles et personne ne sait
Que faire, ni quand elle prit son envol.

Une mêlée de furets, peut-on lui dire
Quand courir et que poursuivre.

Pagaille monstrueuse, diabolique et noire,
Une horde de renards à l'attaque.

Pagaille monstrueuse, pagaille monstrueuse

Un piqué de piverts se joint à la mêlée,
Pagaille monstrueuse, en une journée.

Une conjuration de corbeaux, un complot de corneilles.
Quand tout cela a-t-il commencé ? Personne ne le sait,

Sauf

Une bande de baleines
Une harde fracassante de rhinocéros
Une coterie superbe de lions
Une gambade de chèvres
Une troupe malicieuse de singes
Un bondissement de léopards
Un amassement d'ours
Une floraison de faisans
Un nœud de crapauds
Une fête de geais
Un éclat de chatons
Un cacardement d'oies

Et, bien sûr,

Un parlement de chouettes.

Hou-hou, hou-hou.

Carol Barratt
Traduction : Agnès Ausseur

INSTRUMENTATION

Soprano Saxophone (doubling Tenor Saxophone)
Percussion (3)★
Piano duet

★ 1: tambourine, triangle, chekere
2: congas, vibraphone, glockenspiel
3: drum kit, woodblock

Duration: 17 minutes

Performance materials available on hire

to the people of Yoxford

A PARLIAMENT OF OWLS
A celebration of collective nouns

CAROL BARRATT
(b 1945)

KARL JENKINS
(b 1944)

I – Irresistible and noisy

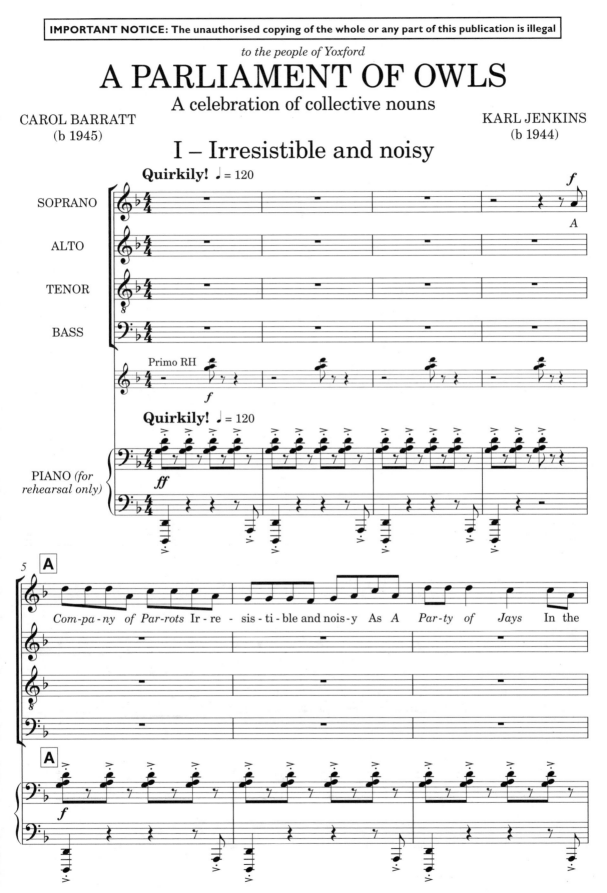

15138

SOPRANO & ALTO div in 3

Ir-re - sis-ti-ble and noi-sy As *A*

Ir-re - sis-ti-ble and noi-sy As *A*

Ir-re - sis-ti-ble and noi-sy As *A*

Chat-ters, chat-ters, chat-ters as it plays.

Chat-ters, chat-ters, chat-ters as it plays.

unis
Chat-ters, chat-ters, chat-ters as it plays.

Chat-ters, chat-ters, chat-ters chat-ters, chat-ters,

chat-ter, chat-ter, chat-ters, chat-ters, chat-ters, chat-ter, chat-ter, chat-ters,

II – Quietly sitting still

Majestically and thoughtfully ♩ = 60

A Par - lia - ment of Owls

Meets from time to time

III – Monstrous mayhem

Manically ♩. = 135

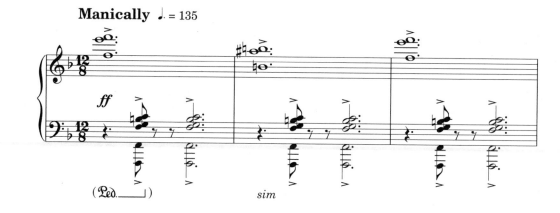

Mon-strous may-hem, all in a day.

Mon-strous may-hem, all in a day.

Mon-strous may-hem, all in a day.

Mon-strous may-hem, all in a day.

An Un-

An Un-

An Un-

An Un-

42

130

tu - whit   tu - whoo,   tu - whit   tu - whoo,   tu - whit   tu -

tu - whit   tu - whoo,   tu - whit   tu - whoo,   tu - whit   tu -

-whit   tu - whoo,   tu - whit   tu - whoo,   tu - whit   tu - whoo,

-whit   tu - whoo,   tu - whit   tu - whoo,   tu - whit   tu - whoo,

132

lunga *mf*

-whoo,   tu - whit tu - whoo,   tu - whit tu - whoo,   tu - whoo.

-whoo,   tu - whit tu - whoo,   tu - whit tu - whoo,   tu - whoo.

tu - whit tu - whoo,   tu - whit tu - whoo,   tu - whit tu - whoo.

tu - whit tu - whoo,   tu - whit tu - whoo,   tu - whit tu - whoo.

Choral music by Karl Jenkins

Stabat Mater
Vocal score (Contralto solo, SATB & piano)
ISMN: 979-0-060-11952-1

Requiem
Vocal score (SATB & piano)
ISMN: 979-0-060-11684-1
Available separately:
Pie Jesu (SATB & piano)
ISMN: 979-0-060-11883-8
Pie Jesu (SSA & piano)
ISMN: 979-0-060-11887-6
Farewell
ISMN: 979-0-060-11886-9
Three Haikus (SATB & piano)
ISMN: 979-0-060-11888-3

The Armed Man: A Mass for Peace
Complete vocal score (SATB & piano)
ISMN: 979-0-060-11545-5
Choral suite vocal score (SATB & piano)
ISMN: 979-0-060-11410-6

Adiemus I: Songs of Sanctuary
Full score
ISMN: 979-0-060-10887-7
Vocal score (SSAA & piano)
ISMN: 979-0-060-10374-2
Pack of ten vocal scores (SSAA & piano)
ISMN: 979-0-060-10501-2

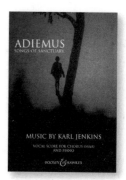

Adiemus
The first movement of
Songs of Sanctuary
Vocal score (SATB & piano)
ISMN: 979-0-060-10671-2
Vocal score (SSAA & piano)
ISMN: 979-0-060-10473-2

Adiemus II: Cantata mundi (choral suite)
Full score
ISMN: 979-0-060-10888-4
Vocal score (SSA & piano)
ISMN: 979-0-060-10669-9
Pack of ten vocal scores (SSA & piano)
ISMN: 979-0-060-10711-5

Adiemus III: Dances of Time (3 movements)
Vocal score (SSA & piano with optional recorder & percussion)
ISMN: 979-0-060-11239-3

Adiemus: Vocalise (5 movements)
Vocal score (SSA & piano)
ISMN: 979-0-060-11623-0

Cantilena
Vocal score (SATB & piano)
ISMN: 979-0-060-11063-4
Vocal score (SSA & piano)
ISMN: 979-0-060-11064-1

A Celebration of Christmas
Vocal score (SSA & piano)
ISMN: 979-0-060-10832-7
Pack of ten vocal scores (SSA & piano)
ISMN: 979-0-060-10833-4
Vocal score (SATB & piano)
ISMN: 979-0-060-10834-1
Pack of ten vocal scores (SATB & piano)
ISMN: 979-0-060-10835-8

Dewi Sant (Saint David)
Vocal score (SATB & piano)
ISMN: 979-0-060-11287-4

Gaudete (carol)
Vocal score (SSAATTBB – a cappella with optional percussion)
ISMN: 979-0-060-11928-6

Jubilate Deo
Vocal score (SATB & organ)
ISMN: 979-0-060-11628-5

Praise
Vocal score (TTBB & piano)
ISMN: 979-0-060-10746-7
Pack of ten vocal scores (SATB & piano)
ISMN: 979-0-060-10835-8

Te Deum
Vocal score (SATB & piano)
ISMN: 979-0-060-12031-2

BOOSEY & HAWKES

Boosey & Hawkes Music Publishers Ltd
www.boosey.com